Know the Game Series

Life Saving

Published by EP Publishing Limited
Printed in Great Britain by J. S. Speight Ltd.
Guiseley, Yorks.

GW01018128

CONTENTS

LIFE SAVING

About this Book

A few years ago an enquiry was made into the circumstances in which people lost their lives through drowning. This included people of all ages. It was found that the victims could be placed in three groups:

(a) Those drowned within easy reach of safety — a raft, the river bank, a nearby boat — or because they were unable to keep themselves afloat while awaiting an oncoming rescuer.

Everyone should learn to swim.

(b) Those who found themselves in difficulties where other swimmers were present, yet these, though anxious to help, had neither the knowledge nor the skill to effect a rescue.

Everyone should learn life saving methods.

(c) Those who had been brought to the shore still alive but were left to die because no one present was able to supply efficient resuscitation.

Everyone should learn how to give resuscitation.

If you read this book you will realise that it is quite simple to learn and practise these basic requirements. It needs only a little effort for you to become a more useful member of society, one able to help in an emergency.

The Royal Life Saving Society

Since 1891 the Royal Life Saving Society has been giving instruction to swimmers on ways of saving people who are in danger of drowning. To encourage swimmers to acquire the necessary knowledge and skill, it arranges suitable tests and it awards certificates and medals to those who satisfy the official examiners.

You should learn under supervision.

If you are a moderately skilful swimmer and attend an official class under one of the Society's instructors, this book should help you to prepare for the following awards:

(a) The Safety Awards.

(b) The Elementary Life Saving Award.

(c) The Intermediate Life Saving Award.

These Proficiency Awards are an introduction to the Bronze Medallion, which is the basic award of the Society and which can be taken at the age of thirteen years and over. Full details of the Bronze Medallion and all other awards can be found in the Society's official Handbook.

Your own safety — and that of others

This may seem a selfish start to our instruction, yet, as you will see, what you will do for your own safety will, at the same time, make you more capable of helping others.

For example, you may have to enter the water from a height, swim while wearing most of your clothes, or remain almost stationary at one spot, either to await a helper who is coming to your assistance or to consider where you should go down to bring up someone from below the surface.

Straddle jump (above)

Compact jump

Entering the water

If the water conditions are unknown, a cautious feet first entry is safest. If entry from a height is unavoidable, it should be feet first and as shallow as possible. Wade, if possible, before starting to swim.

Jump Entries

(a) Straddle Jump — for Shallow Entry

Spring forward into the water your legs spread wide apart to the front and back. Flex your knees slightly and lean forward to an angle of about 40°. Extend your arms sideways and slightly forward, elbows bent a little. Keep your head in line with your body. DO NOT USE THIS ENTRY FROM HEIGHTS OVER ONE METRE

(b) Compact Jump for Entry from Height

Step forward and hold your legs together in line with your trunk. Flex your knees and ankles slightly. Hold your arms tightly to the side or cross them over your chest. As you hit the surface breathe out strongly through the nose. Slow your descent into the water by spreading your arms and kicking.

Swimming in clothes

Though speed is obviously essential when someone is in need of help, you should, before entering the water, take off all heavy or outer garments, shoes, coat, etc.; you will be surprised to find how much even under-clothing will impede your swimming. You should, therefore, practise swimming in clothes at every opportunity to get the *feel* of this, and so learn to cover distance while keeping up a useful speed. You don't want to be exhausted when you reach the victim; that might mean two lives lost instead of one. To start with, swimming in pyjamas is suggested especially as most swimming bath authorities permit this, provided the articles are clean.

Remaining at, or near, one spot

Treading water or lying on your back and sculling are skills which will enable you to keep afloat while using little energy. Why, one may ask, does a human body float at all when practically all the materials of which it is made, fat being the exception, are heavier than water? You will float when your lungs contain sufficient air and your mouth and nose remain above water, enabling you to breathe. You will see, therefore, the importance of the position of your body when you are floating, sculling or treading water.

Treading water

Treading water with your body upright is simply a method by which your nose and mouth are kept above the water. Either your legs, arms, or both acting together can keep you afloat. You can do this by making a leg movement similar to that used in the breast stroke. Crawl swimmers may use their own leg movement though they are likely to find this more tiring.

You can assist by pressing down with your palms against the water, turning your wrists outwards as you do so. Keep your head tilted back in a comfortable position so that your nose and mouth remain above the surface of the water.

It is important not to raise your arms above the water unnecessarily as this might well cause you to sink. To attract attention, signal with one arm only and tread water more vigorously to avoid going under.

Sculling

This is a pleasant way of keeping your body afloat with your face above the surface. Start by hooking your toes under some support at the side of the bath (the bar or the top step of the exit ladder) and lie back on the water with your hands at your sides. Alternatively, you might get a friend to support your head lightly as you lie back in the

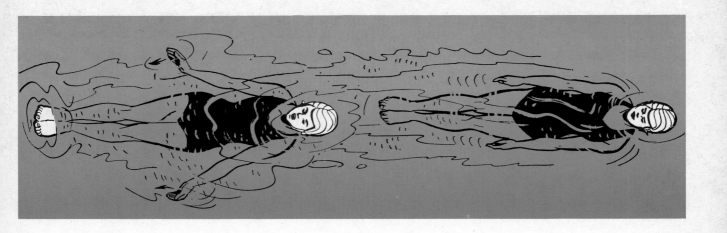

water. A slight push off will set you gliding across the bath head first. Keep your body horizontal but relaxed, your hips up, your legs together, your toes pointed and showing just above the surface. By looking towards your toes without raising your head, making as it were a double chin, you will find your toes will come up to the surface and peep through.

For head-first sculling, keep your arms straight and close to the sides of your body, with your wrists loose. Cup your hands and with a continuous circular movement push the water towards your feet.

For feet-first sculling, reverse the movement and push the water towards your head.

Remember in either case to point your toes and look towards them without raising your head. This will give you a relaxed position and help to keep your legs up.

Diving from the surface

No doubt your first efforts at diving will have been made from the bath side or from one of the lower diving boards. But there are times when it may be necessary to dive from the surface of the water itself, when there will be nothing solid to push against. A surface dive is used to recover a body or other object from below the surface.

The commonest form of surface dive is that made head first; you can see where you are going, have your hands free to grasp objects or to ward off obstructions.

But first you will find it helpful to try making a 'handstand' in the water at the shallow end of the bath. Stand where the water is about breast high and stretch your hands before you. Take a deep breath, thrust your arms deep in the water and with the hands turned as if to make a breast stroke, pull *upwards* towards the surface. As you do this, turn your head and shoulders sharply down into the water, raise your hips and lift your legs clear of the water. Your body will thus be straightened and your hands rest on the bottom of the bath. Your legs should be kept together, toes pointed upwards.

If you pull too hard you will over-balance, but if you do not pull hard enough you will not bring your legs above the surface. It is the weight of your legs above the water which helps to take you down. With practice you will learn just how hard to pull and soon be able to stand on your hands on the bottom with your body in a straight line; you may even be able to walk a few steps.

THE HEAD-FIRST SURFACE DIVE

Your hand-stand was started with your arms extended as they would be during the breast-stroke glide. This is the position from which to start your surface dive. Then thrust your arms, head and shoulders deep into the water, bending at the hips as in the hand-stand, and raise your legs vertically. This will bring your body into line and help to take you down.

To bring up an object from the bottom, swim, preferably breast stroke, to a position about six feet from the point immediately above the object and then make your surface dive. Be prepared to swim down if the dive does not take you deep enough, and keep your eyes open throughout.

Undressing in the water

You will have discovered that even with heavy garments and shoes removed, any clothing makes swimming more difficult. It may help, if you are likely to be in the water for any length of time, to remove clothes which are a hindrance to you.

Generally speaking, clothes can be taken off in one of three ways: jacket fashion, by being pulled over the head, or by being lowered from the legs.

Articles like jackets present little difficulty; you can take them off, while treading water, much as if you were on dry land.

Those which come over the head should be rolled up closely under the armpits; it is then possible, by one quick lift, to get the roll over the head.

Garments (trousers, etc.) which have to fall from off the legs usually do so if you make kicking movements as in treading water. If you first undo your belt you can start these movements while taking off your upper garments, and then give such help as may be necessary with your hands. Naturally, unbuttoning, untying of tapes, stretching of elastics, etc., must be given attention first to make removal possible.

Special caution is needed when removing over the head clothing made of nylon-type material. Rolling first, as suggested above, prevents a dangerous flat sheet of material from covering the mouth.

Leaving the water without assistance

At most swimming baths short step-ladders are placed at the ends, so that getting out presents no great difficulty. You should, however, accustom yourself to getting out from *any* spot round the edge of the bath without help. You will then be prepared if you need to get out of water under similar circumstances elsewhere.

The secret is to make use of the lifting power of the water. Place your hands on the edge and with the help of a breast stroke kick or push off from the bottom, pull yourself up until your arms are straight and you can get one leg over the top, from which position you can easily climb out.

THE R.L.S.S. SAFETY AWARDS

If you have practised the swimming skills we have so far described, you should find yourself nearly ready to obtain one, or both, of the Safety Awards (see page 37).

Swimming strokes useful in life saving

BACK-STROKE, WITHOUT USE OF ARMS

Though you may be a competent swimmer, you may not have practised a stroke which has an important role in many of the methods of towing which can be used to bring someone to safety. It is a back-stroke, the legs only being used.

Lying in the water, keep the upper part of your legs in line with your body and lower your feet from the knees; your shin bones will then be nearly vertical. The position of your feet is most important; bend them upwards into a flatfooted position and turn them outwards as in the diagram. Now straighten and open your legs and bring back to their starting position. The movement is a short, continuous circular action from the knees, the insteps and the shins pressing against the water.

Keep your chin well in and practise swimming several lengths, resting your hands on the base of your chest.

This stroke produces steady progress, without jerking, but it is somewhat tiring. Over a long distance it might have to be varied with rests between strokes.

THE SIDE-STROKE

The side-stroke is recommended for use with several of the towing methods. It is less strenuous than most other strokes, so can be kept up for a longer distance. Moreover, as your face rests upon the water, breathing is easy even in choppy water and you can also get a clear view ahead.

The gliding position. Your body is straight, lying on one side, with your face resting in the water. Though either side may be used, let us assume you to be on your right side, the right arm extended fully beyond the head with the palm of the hand downwards. The left arm will be along the left side of the body.

Arm action. The right arm makes its stroke by pulling through the water with a shallow circular sweep underneath the right shoulder.

Except when towing someone, the left arm glides forward, palm downwards, to a position just forward and below your face, the elbow being kept close to the body and well bent. It then makes a backward pull just below the surface and finishes alongside the thigh.

Leg action. As the right arm is completing its recovery, the legs are opened from the hips, the knees bending. They are then extended and snapped together in a scissor movement. As you are on your side, the movement of both legs will be nearly parallel to the surface of the water.

Reach, throw, wade, row, swim and tow

Examine the pictures on this page. They will show you that it is not always necessary, or the best action, to enter the water to save someone else.

The methods of rescue should be considered in this order: REACH — THROW — WADE — ROW — SWIM taking a support — SWIM and TOW.

Everyone can give help in some way. A weak or non-swimmer can REACH, THROW or WADE. He can go for help. He can assist in resuscitation and after-care.

WARNING
The approach to a victim must be made with great caution to avoid his clutch, which can be vice-like through fear.

When victim is near the bank, etc. Try to REACH him

When farther out THROW a rope or support

When some way out in shallow water WADE to reach or throw

When a long way out  ROW if possible (or use power boat)

Otherwise provided you can swim well  SWIM taking support

(if you can't fetch help)

Or if a trained life saver as a last resort SWIM and TOW (preferably with a towing aid)

Defensive methods

These skills are designed to allow the rescuer to 'stand off' a dangerous victim or avoid a sudden clutch.

REVERSE

The basic defensive technique to reverse the position of the body while still out of the subject's reach and to move the rescuer quickly away from danger.

From the prone swimming position, press down with your hands, fling your head and shoulders back, tuck your knees towards your chest and scull backwards with arms and hands. Kick vigorously to move away from the subject.

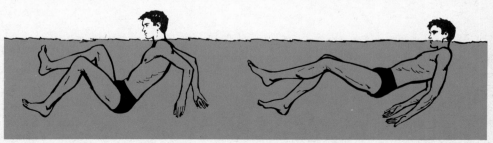

Single leg block

SINGLE LEG BLOCK

If the subject is within range when attempting a clutch, as you 'reverse', block his attempt by *thrusting* against his shoulder or chest with one leg. (In practice apply the foot to shoulder.)

COUNTER

Used if the leg is grasped while attempting a single block. Pull the subject under water using the grasped leg and move over the top of him. When he is below you take him by the chin, turn and lift him into a towing position.

DUCK AWAY

To avoid a sudden clutch at close quarters immediately lower your head and push upwards with your hands against his hips, waist, chest or arms, forcing him away. Speed and aggression are essential.

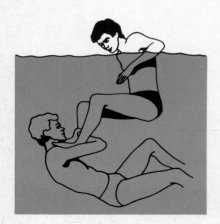
Counter

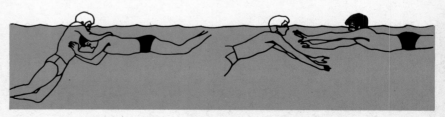
Duck away

Releases

These skills should not be necessary in a planned swimming rescue unless a wrong assessment has been made. If circumstances do occur in which a clutch is applied an immediate vigorous release is vital.

In all cases care should be taken to maintain control of and contact with the subject immediately after the release has been made.

Push up break (a) and (b)

PUSH UP BREAK

Used when the rescuer is seized from the front:

(a) If the head and neck are clutched, tuck the chin into the shoulder and exert leverage upwards on the subject's elbows or upper arms or under his armpits.

(b) If a pinion clutch, tuck the chin into the shoulder, force your elbows upwards and outwards grasping the subject under the armpits or on his trunk. Take a deep breath and push him upwards getting out of his clutch by submerging. While submerged turn the subject to a towing position.

Pull Control

Used when the rescuer's wrist or arm is clutched by both hands of the subject. Move yourself towards the subject by pulling slightly downwards and outwards with the gripped arm. Aim to go past his shoulder and as you do so give a powerful leg kick raising yourself above and behind him, at the same time swing your free arm round the back of his neck taking a firm grip on his chin. In this position you may be able to pull your arm free, if not the subject can still be towed easily by the chin.

Pull control

(b) Arm Pull

Used if 'pull control' cannot be effected. Clench the fist of the gripped arm. With your free arm reach over or under, according to the grip, between the victim's arms. Take hold of the clenched fist and pull up or down applying pressure against his thumb joints. There is a momentary loss of contact, so re-establish control **immediately** by grasping and turning him into a towing position.

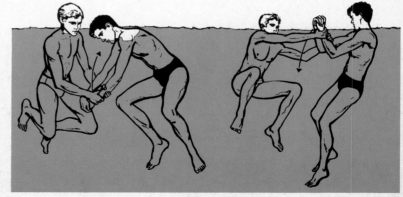

Arm pull

Note: When the rescuer is seized from behind in any position he must immediately protect his throat by forcing his chin down.

ELBOW BREAK

Used against clutches above the rescuer's elbows.

Drop your chin quickly on to your chest to protect your throat. Grasp one of his wrists with your opposite hand (left wrist - right hand, or the other way round) and his elbow with your other hand. Then force the elbow up and pull downwards and inwards on his wrist. Turn your head away from the elbow you are forcing up and duck underneath his arm, holding on to his wrist until you have turned it behind his back. Keep it there until you have him in a towing position.

JOINT PRESSURE BREAK

Used against clutches pinning the rescuer's elbows.

Grip the subject's thumbs or fingers and force his hands apart by pressure against the joints.

Spread the subject's arms wide apart and move behind him taking care not to be clutched again.

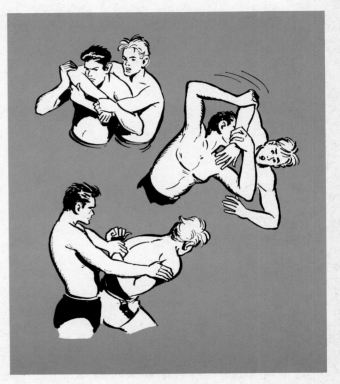

Recovery from the bottom

If the subject has sunk to the bottom, take hold of him by the head or under the arms with both hands. If the bottom is firm, push off from it vigorously and, using the back-stroke leg kick, bring him to the surface.

If the bottom is soft or muddy, grasp the victim in the same way. Do not step on the bottom in case you get stuck, and use only the leg kick to get him to the surface.

Supporting a person

There may be occasions when it will be necessary for you to support a person for a short time until help arrives.

When you can tread water strongly, try to support a friend without any help from him; you can do this from behind by grasping him under the arms or by the head, keeping his face above the water.

Towing methods

There are a number of ways of towing a person through the water and you will have to decide which is the best one to use, depending on whether he is conscious, unconscious or injured; whether he is calm or in a panic and likely to clutch at you; on the state of the water, whether it is rough or not; on the direction and strength of the tide, current or wind. With all tows remember to keep the subject's face clear of the water and in the case of contact tows, your hand or arm clear of his throat.

NON-CONTACT TOW—using an aid

Used with a conscious subject.

With rescuer and subject holding opposite ends of the aid, tow using either side stroke or life-saving back stroke.

With a non-rigid aid, the subject may be more easily towed on his back.

CONTACT TOW

CHIN TOW

Used with a subject needing firm control.

From behind, pass your arm over the subject's shoulder. Cup his chin in your hand with his head turned into your shoulder. Secure a firm grip by pressing your arm into his shoulder. Use your free arm to help you swim.

Shoulder Restraint

If the subject struggles, pass your free arm under his armpit and take a firm grip on his shoulder from the front.

Breathing Restraint

If the shoulder restraint does not control the subject, grip his nose and cover his mouth with the hand cupping his chin, to stop him breathing. He will then instinctively pull your arm down on to his chest and hold it there; try to grip him under the armpit to secure your hold. The tow can continue in this position, and you may be able to resume swimming with the arm which has been applying the shoulder restraint.

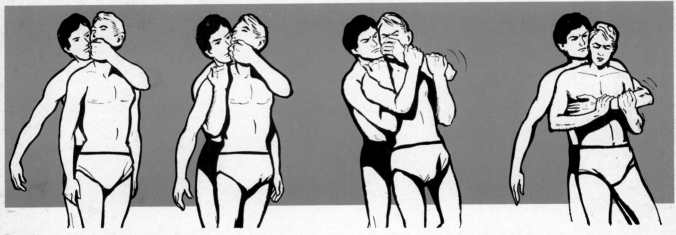

Cup victim's chin, pressing your arm into his shoulder

Pass your free arm under his armpit and grip his shoulder

If victim continues to struggle, cover his nose and mouth with your hand

When he pulls your arm down, continue towing

CROSS CHEST TOW

Used in rough or difficult conditions with the side stroke.

Place one arm over the subject's shoulder across his chest, clamping your elbow firmly down, and grasp him under the opposite armpit. While swimming keep your upper hip close to the small of his back.

EXTENDED TOW BY HAIR, CLOTHING OR CHIN

These are methods which you can keep up over a long distance, using the side-stroke.

Take a firm grip on the subject's hair and tow him at arm's length, or take a firm grip on the clothing at the back of the subject's neck, making sure you do not restrict his breathing, or cup your upper hand under the subject's chin, keeping his face above the water by adjusting your arm or wrist as necessary.

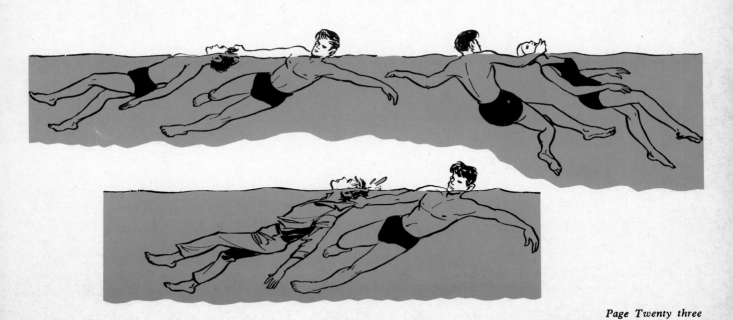

Landing a rescued person

How a rescued person is taken from the water will depend on whether he is conscious or unconscious, whether the water is shallow or deep, and whether the landing place is shelving or steep.

If the landing place is shelving, the subject can be assisted to walk out if he is conscious, or, if not, floated in on his back through the shallow water, during which time resuscitation can be given.

THE 'SUPPORT' POSITION

Used to secure the subject in a position of safety against a firm support with his face out of the water.

From behind, pass your arms under the subject's arm-pits and secure him with a firm grip on the bar, side or other support such as boat, steep bank, landing stage, etc.

The "support" position

THE STIRRUP METHOD (see facing page)

This can be used when the subject is able to give some help.

Support him against the side, bend down, cup your free hand and allow him to put his foot or knee in it and give him a helping lift on to the top. When in shallow water, if he does not need to be supported use both hands to make the stirrup.

The Stirrup method

LANDING—RESCUER FIRST

When the subject is unable to help, the rescuer places the subject's hands on the top one above the other, holding him there with his face above the water while climbing out.

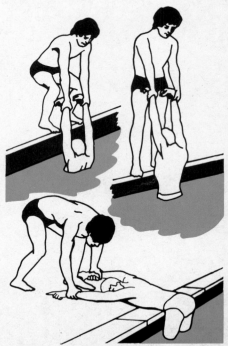

There are two methods of getting the subject out unaided.

THE STRAIGHT ARM METHOD FROM DEEP WATER

Grip the subject's wrists and lift him up and down a few times, bending and straightening your knees, making sure to keep his face above the water, then lift him up and over the edge so that he rests on his chest. With one hand firmly on his back to secure him, use your other hand to lift his legs on to the side.

FROM SHALLOW WATER

This method can be used without the preparatory movements. With caution, lift the subject up and fold him gently over the edge. Avoid bumping his head as you lower him.

If you are not able to lift his legs on to the side from this position, get back into the water to do so.

THE CROSSED ARM METHOD

When you are out of the water, cross your arms and hold the subject's wrists. Lift him up and down a few times, bending and straightening your knees, making sure to keep his face above the water. Then lift him from the water, uncrossing your arms as you do so. This will bring him into a sitting position on the edge facing the water. Take great care to avoid injuring the subject against the side.

Resuscitation

Resuscitation is the essential first-aid treatment required by the victim of any accident which restricts the intake of oxygen. It must be applied without any delay if it is to be successful.

GOLDEN RULES

(a) Keep calm.

(b) Get air into the lungs by starting resuscitation immediately.

(c) Send for help if possible.

RESPIRATION AND THE CIRCULATION OF THE BLOOD

Elementary knowledge of the working of those parts of the body concerned with respiration and the circulation of blood will help the trained life saver to understand more fully how and why methods of resuscitation will be effective.

Every cell of the body needs oxygen for survival and will be damaged and eventually die without it. The cells of the brain are damaged especially quickly by a shortage of oxygen. This is why it is so important to start resuscitation as soon as possible after normal respiration has stopped, whatever the cause.

Air, which is composed of one fifth oxygen, enters the body through the mouth and nose and passes through the throat into the windpipe. The upper part of the windpipe is protected by a special flap, which allows entry of air but prevents the entry of other materials, such as food or water, etc.

Passing down the windpipe, air enters the lungs which, with the heart and the largest blood vessels (arteries and veins), are protected by the ribs, which form a strong cage of the chest. In the lungs oxygen passes from the air into the blood and carbon dioxide from the blood into the air in the lungs, to be breathed out.

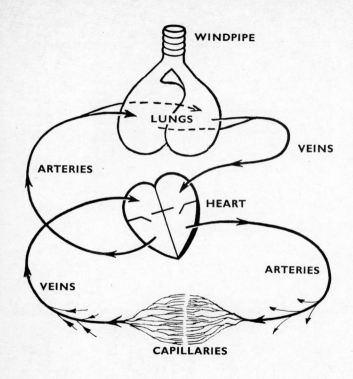

WINDPIPE

LUNGS

VEINS

ARTERIES

HEART

ARTERIES

VEINS

CAPILLARIES

The rate of breathing is about 15 to 20 per minute, but gets much faster when more oxygen is needed by the cells of the body during exercise, such as swimming or running.

The heart is a pump divided into two parts. One part pumps blood to the lungs and the other pumps it through the rest of the body. The tubes which take the blood from the heart are the arteries. The blood returns to the heart through the veins. The arteries divide and sub-divide, getting smaller and smaller, finishing as very small tubes called capillaries. It is from these capillaries that the oxygen passes from the blood to the body cells and it is here also that the blood receives the carbon dioxide from the same cells. The blood then passes from the capillaries via the veins back to the heart.

A similar process takes place when blood is pumped to the lungs.

If you would like more information about the Royal Life Saving Society and its work, publicity material is available free of charge.

The main teaching handbooks are:
"Life Saving and Water Safety"   50p
"Emergency Resuscitation"   30p
Plus Current Postage

From : —

    The Royal Life Saving Society,
    14, Devonshire Street, London, W1N 2AT.

A 16 mm. colour sound film illustrating many of the rescues in action is available for sale or hire from—

    Explorer Films,
    58, Stratford Road,
    Bromsgrove,
    Worcestershire.

Phone : Bromsgrove 3566.

When resuscitation is needed

Resuscitation may be needed after accidents involving gas poisoning, electric shock and the effects of lightning, suffocation, hanging, strangulation or where there is something blocking the victim's throat.

Getting help

When faced with an emergency requiring resuscitation it is important to send someone for the police and ambulance, but do not leave the patient to do this yourself. Police or ambulance personnel will see that he is taken to a doctor or to the hospital. Every victim of an accident who has required resuscitation must be taken to hospital as soon as possible whether he has been revived or is still unconscious.

Turning a patient

If you need to turn a patient on to his back to start resuscitation, kneel by his side, stretch out the arm nearest to you and grasp his far shoulder with one hand and his hip with the other, at the same time clamping his hand under yours. With a steady pull with both arms roll him over against your thighs. Lower him gently to the ground, supporting his head and shoulder as you do so, and then replace his other arm by his side.

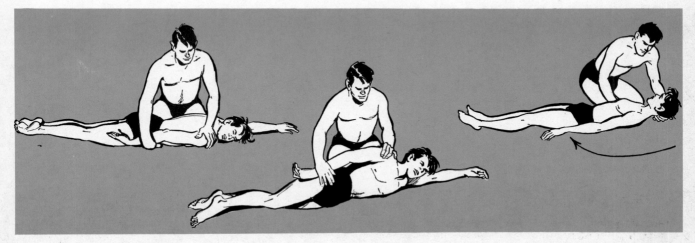

Resuscitation — The Expired Air Method

The diagrams below show the difference between the air you breathe in (inspired air) and that which you breathe out (expired air). Both contain oxygen. Although the expired air has less oxygen there is still plenty left to help a person in need of it. You can breathe this expired air with its valuable oxygen into a patient's lungs through his nose, his mouth or, in the case of a small child, through both at the same time. Immediately before giving resuscitation, breathe deeply yourself with your mouth open, to build up your own oxygen content. Remember, the heart may continue to beat only for a few minutes after breathing has stopped, and, therefore, **it is vital that resuscitation is started without the slightest delay.**

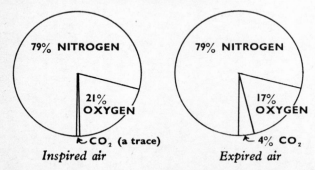

Inspired air *Expired air*

Lay the patient on his back and take a quick look at his mouth and throat, removing any obvious obstructions.

Tilt the patient's head back *as far as possible;* this will stretch his neck and keep open the air-way. Seal his nose with your fingers and blow into his mouth.

Start with four quick breaths to build up rapidly the oxygen in his blood and then slow down to twelve to fifteen breaths per minute. After each breath turn your head to see that his chest falls, whilst breathing in deeply ready to blow again. If the chest does not move, check that the mouth and throat are clear, that the head is tilted back as far as possible and then blow again.

An alternative method is to seal your mouth over his nose and blow into his lungs while supporting his chin and keeping his mouth closed with one hand.

With children and babies small puffs only should be given at the rate of twenty per minute. Because of the serious risk of injury, never blow violently into a baby's lungs.

If air enters the patient's stomach, press it lightly with his head turned away to one side.

The method may be practised either on a manikin or by using another person. In the latter case, of course, no air should actually be blown into the supposed patient. The operator should lean over, with his own chin slightly above the patient's face but well beyond it. He can then blow out expired air without unpleasantness to the person who is acting as his patient.

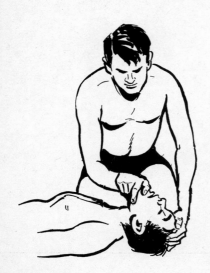

*Tilt head
back fully*

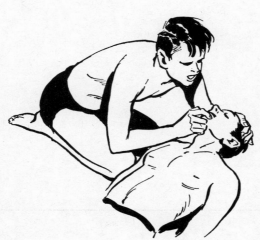

*Breathe deeply
yourself*

*Seal his nose and
blow into his mouth*

Action if vomiting occurs

Should the patient show signs of vomiting, turn him away from you on to his side and support him against your thighs. Allow his head to hang down to prevent the vomit from entering his windpipe.

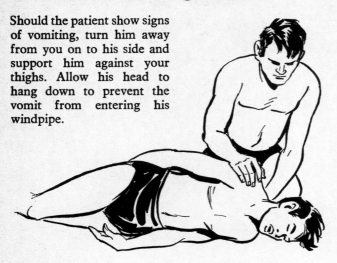

Demonstrating and Practising Expired Air Resuscitation

1. Practise breathing deeply in and out at five-second intervals.

2. Learn to put the head in the right position by practising with a partner. Close his mouth and support his jaw by placing your thumb and forefinger respectively down either side of his jaw bone; curl your other fingers and fit the knuckle of your second finger under his jaw. Make sure that your curled fingers do not press on his throat.

3. Get used to adopting the correct position for the operator by kneeling close beside your partner.

4. Take every chance of practising on a training mannikin or mask.

5. For practice and demonstration purposes where a training aid is not available, lean over your partner and breath down past his far cheek.

Expired Air Resuscitation—Techniques in Water

In each case use the mouth to nose method. Close the victim's mouth and support his jaw in the normal manner for mouth to nose resuscitation, using that hand to extend the head and

STANDING IN SHALLOW WATER

support the victim's trunk either between his shoulder blades or under his far armpit with your other hand, or

SUPPORTED IN DEEP WATER

support the victim with your other arm behind his neck with your hand gripping the bar or side.

Note: For practice and demonstration purposes for the above techniques, the rescuer's mouth should be applied to the subject's forehead.

The R.L.S.S. Proficiency Awards

The full conditions of all the examinations are given in the official R.L.S.S. Handbook. They should be studied by candidates who are under instruction before applying for the examination.

If you wish to join a class, write to the Secretary of your local branch of the R.L.S.S. or, if you do not know his address, to the R.L.S.S. Headquarters, 14 Devonshire Street, London W.1.

RESUSCITATION—THE BASIC TEST

This is the test for all awards up to and including the Intermediate.

EXAMINATION SYLLABUS

Demonstrate to the satisfaction of the examiner the expired air method showing:

(a) The correct positioning of the subject;

(b) the mouth to nose technique;

(c) the mouth to mouth technique;

(d) the action to be taken in case of;
    (i) vomit
    (ii) recovery, placing the subject in the coma position.

WATER SAFETY AWARD

Object: to test knowledge of the rules of water safety applicable to inexperienced and non-swimmers, the ability to give simple basic help to someone in difficulty in the water and elementary resuscitation.

1. WATER SAFETY

Show a knowledge of water safety for non-swimmers by answering questions from the water safety rules (including the advice to parents), see inside back cover.

2. ELEMENTARY RESUSCITATION

Complete the basic test.

3. ELEMENTARY RESCUE

Demonstrate on land two methods of reaching someone in difficulties in the water, using:

(a) a branch or length of wood;

(b) two articles of clothing tied together.

Demonstrate on land throwing to within reach of a stationary subject over a distance of 20 feet:

(a) an unweighted rope;

(b) a large inflated ring or similar object.

THE SAFETY AWARDS

Object: to test swimming competence and preparatory life-saving skills.

Candidates Dress for water test

Ladies and girls: a dress, or blouse and slacks; swimwear.
Men and boys: trousers and shirt; swimwear.
Pyjamas with long trousers are an acceptable alternative for both males and females.

PRELIMINARY SAFETY AWARD

1. RESUSCITATION

Complete the basic test (see page 36).

2. WATER TEST

Carry out the following tests as a continuous sequence:
(a) Enter water feet first and swim 50 yards.
(b) Tread water for 1 minute.
(c) In deep water remove all clothing except swimwear.
(d) Swim 200 yards by any stroke.
(e) Scull head first for 10 yards.
(f) Surface dive in a depth of not less than 4 feet and use feet to push off the bottom.

ADVANCED SAFETY AWARD

1. RESUSCITATION

Complete the basic test (see page 36).

2. WATER TEST

Carry out the following tests as a continuous sequence:

(a) Enter the water feet first and tread water for 3 minutes (1 minute legs only, 2 minutes arms only).

(b) Swim 100 yards in less than 4 minutes.

(c) In deep water remove all clothing except swimwear in less than 20 seconds.

(d) Swim 200 yards on the back without use of arms or artificial aids.

(e) Swim 200 yards by any stroke other than back stroke.

(f) Scull head first for 20 yards.

(g) Leave deep water without the use of steps or assistance,

(h) Recover an object (5 to 10 lbs.) from a depth of 6 feet (or nearest depth available, but not less than 5 feet). Land the object.

ELEMENTARY AWARD

Object: to test self preservation, swimming competence and non-contact rescue as a preparatory stage to higher awards. The holder is **not** qualified to attempt a swimming rescue in deep water.

1. WATER SAFETY
Answer six questions on water safety.

2. RESUSCITATION
Complete the basic test (see page 36).

3. WATER TEST
(a) Using an aid demonstrate a reaching rescue. The subject shall be in deep water, six feet from the side. The subject should be carefully pulled to the side.

(b) Demonstrate a throwing rescue using an unweighted rope over 10 yards. Three attempts are allowed to place the rope within reach of a stationary subject. The subject should be carefully pulled to the side.

(c) Enter shallow water with a buoyant aid and swim 20 yards to a subject considered to be a weak swimmer. Push the aid to the subject and at a safe distance direct and accompany the subject 20 yards back to the starting point.

(d) Enter the water, surface and swim 10 yards. Recover an object (5 to 10 lbs.) from a depth of at least 4 feet. Bring to the starting point using life saving back stroke.

(e) Swim continuously for 125 yards as follows:
   (i) 50 yards life saving back stroke;
  (ii) 50 yards free style on the front;
 (iii) 25 yards side stroke.

INTERMEDIATE AWARD

Object: to test the ability of the more competent swimmer at a stage preparatory to the Bronze Medallion. The holder is not qualified to attempt a contact rescue in deep water.

If candidates have gained the Elementary Award within the previous 12 months they are excused parts 3 (a) and (b).

1. WATER SAFETY and RESCUE

Answer six questions on water safety and principles and methods of rescue.

2. RESUSCITATION

Successfully complete the basic test (see page 36).

3. WATER TEST

(a) Elementary Award test 3 (a);

(b) Elementary Award test 3 (b);

(c) With a towing aid enter shallow water as for unknown conditions. Swim 20 yards to the subject.

Tow for 20 yards using the aid. Assist the subject from the water.

(d) Enter deep water with a straddle jump, swim 25 yards to the subject and demonstrate 'the Reverse': then calm, reassure and approach the subject from behind. Tow for 25 yards by either the Cross Chest or Chin Tow (no restraints). On completion of the tow secure the subject in the support position.

(e) Enter shallow water and swim 20 yards. Recover an object (5 to 10 lbs.) from a depth of at least 5 feet. Exchange the object for a subject considered to be unconscious and not breathing.

Tow by an approved method selected by the candidate to water shallow enough to stand in.

Demonstrate mouth-to-nose resuscitation while walking the subject at least 5 yards to the side.

Land the subject, considered to be unconscious but breathing, and place in the coma position.

(f) Swim continuously for 100 yards as follows:
 (i) 50 yards free style on the front;
 (ii) 50 yards side stroke.

The time limit for this test is 2 minutes 30 seconds.

WATER SAFETY RULES.

If you cannot swim — **LEARN.**

Don't play in forbidden or dangerous places such as:
    canal banks;
    gravel pits;
    river banks;
    ponds.

REMEMBER

Home made rafts soon sink.

Ice melts quickly and breaks.

Only go boating with an adult and wear a life jacket.

Do take heed of notice boards.

Do not hang anything over notice boards.

TO BATHE SAFELY

Only do so with your parents' permission and in their sight. Never bathe alone. Do not go in water deeper than waist level. Never bathe just after a meal or when hungry. Use only air beds or rubber rings in a safe place like the paddling pool — otherwise there is a danger of being carried into deep water. Don't fool about in or near water. Don't run on wet surrounds.

If you fall in

Keep calm.

Call for help.

Float on your back.

To attract attention wave one arm only.

If someone else falls in

Look for something to help him out (stick, rope, scarf), lie down so that you will not be pulled in too.

If you cannot reach him, tell him to float on his back or throw any floating object (rubber ring or ball) for him to hold on to, then fetch help.

Always observe these rules and when you are a good swimmer, also learn the safety rules for swimmers.

Disregard of these rules may endanger the rescuer as well as the person in difficulties.